half

past

Time

The Jan Pieńkowski Nursery Books:
Colours, Faces, Food, Homes, Numbers,
Shapes, Time, Weather, Wheels, Yes No

for Daniel

This edition published 2009 by Walker Books Ltd
87 Vauxhall Walk, London SE11 5HJ
10 9 8 7 6 5 4 3 2 1
© 1980, 2009 Jan Pieńkowski

The moral rights of the author/illustrator have been asserted
Lettering by Caroline Austin

Printed in China All rights reserved
British Library Cataloguing in Publication Data is available
ISBN 978-1-4063-1433-5 www.walker.co.uk

WALKER BOOKS
AND SUBSIDIARIES
LONDON · BOSTON · SYDNEY · AUCKLAND

TIME

Jan Pieńkowski

5 o'clock

7 o'clock

8 o'clock

9 o'clock

11 o'clock

noon

4 o'clock

6 o'clock

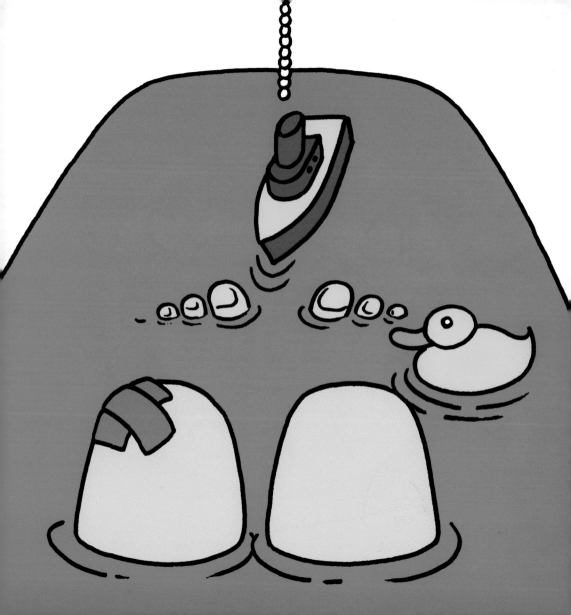

10 o'clock

midnight

what time?

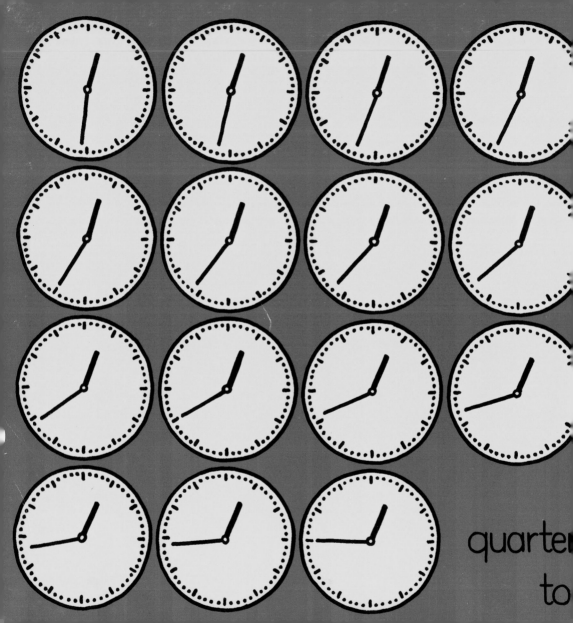

quarter
to